LATIN TRIVIA
QUIZ BOOK

LATIN TRIVIA
QUIZBOOK

LEA CHAMBERS

ROBINSON

LONDON

First published in Great Britain by Robinson,
an imprint of Constable & Robinson Ltd
3 The Lanchesters
162 Fulham Palace Rd
London W6 9ER

A CIP catalogue record of this book is available
from the British Library

ISBN 1-84119-201-5

Design by Tony and Penny Mills

Printed and bound in the EC

CONTENTS

WHO
SAID THAT?

WHO SAID THAT?

1 Which Emperor admitted on his deathbed 'You have won, o man of Galilee!' and to whom was he referring?

2 When friends congratulated this man for his victory over the Romans, he said 'Another such victory and we are done for!' Who was he?

3 Whose poem included the famous line 'I fear the Greeks even when they bear gifts'?

4 *cui bono?* was the maxim of Cassius Longinus but someone else famously used it in an earlier speech. Who was the orator and whom was he defending at the time?

5 One of Wilfred Owen's war poems includes the line *dulce et decorum est pro patria mori*. Which Roman poet was he quoting?

6 *iacta alea est*

   (a) What does this mean?

   (b) Who is believed to have said this and on what occasion?

7 Who prayed 'Lord, give me chastity... but not yet'?

8 Who boasted that he had 'found the city of Rome brick and left it marble'?

9 Who asked, *quis custodiet ipsos custodes?* and what does this mean?

10 Which Emperor declared 'Only the Greeks are worth my genius!'

11 Who said 'Something greater than the *Iliad* is being brought to birth' and what was he referring to?

12 Which poet expressed the idea that 'when Greece had been enslaved, she made a slave of her rough conqueror'?

13 Whose sole desire was '*mens sana in corpore sano*' and what does this mean?

14 *veni, vidi, vici*

   (a) What does this mean?

   (b) Who is believed to have used these words and on what occasion?

15 Who continually urged the Senate with the words *delenda est Carthago* and what do they mean?

16 *o tempora, o mores!*

    (a) What does this mean?

    (b) Who made this lament and on what occasion?

17 Who made the impossible demand 'Quintilius Varus, give me back my legions!'?

18 *qualis artifex pereo!*

    (a) What does this mean?

    (b) Who is believed to have said these words before committing suicide?

19 Which Emperor said 'I wish that the Roman people had just one neck!'

20 Which Roman poet encouraged Epicurean habits among his audience with exhortations such as *nunc est bibendum* and *carpe diem*?

ANIMALS

ANIMALS

1 How is the animal *canis familiaris* better known?

2 What is the more common name for *ursus maritimus*?

3 What can you say about the group of animals known as edentates?

4 What do ungulates have in common?

5 What Latin words do scientists give to the two classifications of animals which rank in order beneath family?

6 What animals make up the *suidae* family?

7 What is the well-known warning that accompanies a mosaic picture of a dog, often found at the entrance to Roman houses?

8 What was the name of the famous Roman horse who had a marble stable, purple blankets and a jewelled collar, as well as his own house, furniture and slaves and whose owner was seriously considering him for Consulship?

9 What is

   (a) a herbivore

   (b) a carnivore

   (c) an omnivore?

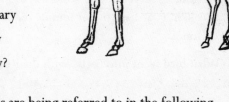

10 What type of creatures live in

   (a) a formicary

   (b) an aviary

   (c) an apiary?

11 What animals are being referred to in the following English adjectives

   (a) bovine   (e) aquiline

   (b) ovine   (f) equine

   (c) canine   (g) vulpine

   (d) feline   (h) leonine?

12 What word describes both the wild ass of central Asia and an ancient military engine for throwing large stones?

13 What class of animals are literally 'creepers'?

14 What is the name given to small invertebrate creatures with bodies which look as if they have been literally 'cut into'?

15 What are *vibrissae* and which animal do they belong to?

16 Why would an arachnophobic run away from the creature known as *lactrodectus mactans*?

17 Can you tell which **three** animals were sacrificed at the Roman festival of Suovetauralia?

18 According to legend, what kind of animal suckled Romulus and Remus?

19 What birds sacred to the goddess Juno were famously excellent guardians of her temple on the Capitoline hill in Rome?

20 What bird went into battle with the Roman army?

THE
ROMANS
IN
BRITAIN

THE ROMANS IN BRITAIN

1 What Roman remains can be found at Housesteads, Northumberland?

2 Which **two** estuaries were linked by the Antonine Wall?

3 Give the modern names of the Roman towns of

   (a) Eboracum

   (b) Camulodunum.

4 Name the landing places of the invading armies of

   (a) Julius Caesar

   (b) Claudius.

5 Which two British cities are linked by the remains of Hadrian's Wall?

6 What were the Roman names for
   (a) Bath

   (b) Chester?

7 Give the name of Boudicca's tribe and the part of Britain in which it was based.

8 Who was Roman governor of Britain at the time of the so-called Boudiccan revolt?

9 Which Roman road runs from London to Wroxeter in Shropshire via St Albans?

10 What did the Romans call

   (a) Anglesey

   (b) the Isle of Wight?

11 Which Roman legion did Boudicca's forces defeat just outside Colchester in AD 60?

12 (a) In which British city can a statue of Boudicca be found?

   (b) Where is she believed to be buried?

13 Which **two** Roman towns were connected by Ermine Street and what are those places called now?

14 Give the name of the town in South Wales where remains of an amphitheatre and Roman military camp have been uncovered.

15 How were two of the legions which came to Britain in AD 43,

   (a) *Legio II* and

   (b) *Legio XX*

   better known?

16 In which British town was Pontius Pilate said to have originated, where an ancient yew tree marks his supposed birthplace?

17 (a) Which British warrior and son of Cunobelinus was killed in a battle at the river Medway in AD 43?

    (b) Name his more famous brother, who escaped alive from this same battle only to be betrayed some time later by Queen Cartimandua and taken to Rome in chains.

18 Which two Roman Emperors died in the city of York?

19 Which university is situated in the town the Romans called Granta?

20 (a) Which Roman historian wrote a biography of Gnaeus Julius Agricola, governor of Britain from AD 78–84?

    (b) In which battle were the Caledonians defeated by a Roman army led by Agricola in AD 84?

FAMOUS
ROMANS

1 How many wives did Julius Caesar have, and what were their names?

2 Which great Roman poet was banished to Tomis, a god-forsaken outpost of the Roman Empire on the Black Sea in AD 8, when he was at the height of his fame?

3 For whom was the first mausoleum built?

4 Who were the members of the first Triumvirate?

5 Who were the members of the second Triumvirate?

6 Who was responsible for reforming the calendar, lengthening the year from 355 to 365 days?

7 Which woman was celebrated by Roman writers for her courage and remarkable self-control and was most famous for stabbing herself and handing the dagger to her husband with the words 'It does not hurt, Paetus'?

8 What was the name of Cleopatra's son by Julius Caesar?

9 Which famous Roman author died in the aftermath of the eruption of the volcano Vesuvius?

10 Which famous commander of the Praetorian Guard grew in influence by successfully eliminating his opponents during the reign of the Emperor Tiberius?

11 Whose epitaph, believed to have been composed on his deathbed, reads as follows:

'Mantua bore me; Calabria snatched me away; now Naples holds me. I sang of pastures, fields and kings.'?

12 What was the name of the island where the Emperor Augustus banished his only daughter Julia in 2 BC for her alleged adulteries?

13 Who went on trial in 61 BC for trespassing on the exclusively female Bona Dea festival disguised as a woman?

14 What was the name of the Thracian gladiator who led a revolt in 73–71 BC with an army which consisted largely of slaves?

15 What title was given to Marcus Porcius Cato, a dominant figure in the political and cultural life of Rome in the first half of the second century BC, who was austere, parsimonious and strict in the moral code he attempted to establish through his speeches and writings?

16 Which Roman poet fought on the losing side at the battle of Philippi in 42 BC but, within four years, had been accepted into the circle of Brutus' enemies?

17 Which Roman statesman, best known for the literary letters which he published, was sent by the Emperor Trajan to govern the province of Bithynia-Pontus and died there c. AD 112?

18 Which correspondent of Cicero, who had been a friend from childhood, was remarkable for his tact, diplomacy and survival instinct during one of the most turbulent periods in Roman history?

19 What was believed to be the real name of the lover whom Catullus calls 'Lesbia' in his poems?

20 What was the relationship between Pliny the Elder and Pliny the Younger?

AGRIPPA

MYTH AND LEGEND

MYTH AND LEGEND

1 Who was the Roman god of wine and revelry?

2 Of what was Vulcan the god?

3 Who were the Roman counterparts of these Greek gods

   (a) Hermes   (d) Eros

   (b) Hestia   (e) Zeus

   (c) Poseidon   (f) Artemis?

4 What Roman god was also known as Dis (short for Dives)?

5 What name did the Romans give to the goddess of the dawn?

6 Who was the mother of

   (a) Mercury

   (b) Apollo and Diana?

7 Which Roman goddess was known as the Cyprian?

8 What was the Roman name of the Greek hero Heracles?

9 What was the name which the Romans gave to the Greek hero Odysseus?

10 Who were the one-eyed giants believed to inhabit the coast of Sicily?

11 In answer to whose prayer did the goddess Venus breathe life into an ivory statue called Galatea?

12 Which god's reign was known to the Romans as the Golden Age, a time of primeval innocence, fruitfulness and peace?

13 Who were the rural demi-gods, believed to inhabit forests and groves, who were usually represented as human but with a goat's tail, pointed ears, horns and hooves?

14 What name was given to certain women in Greek and Roman mythology who were endowed by the god Apollo with the gift of prophecy?

15 Who according to legend were the parents of Romulus and Remus?

16 Which tribe's young women did the early Romans abduct and marry under their king Romulus' instructions?

17 What was the name given to Romulus after he had been raised up to the rank of a god?

18 Give the name of the legendary hero of ancient Rome, who with just two other men held the Sublician bridge against the Etruscan enemy led by Lars Porsenna, while the other Romans broke it down behind him?

19 What were the names of the three brothers who saved and expanded the boundary of Rome by agreeing to fight the three Curiatius brothers from neighbouring Alba Longa?

20 Name the woman who betrayed the citadel of Rome to the Sabine enemy soldiers, in the hope of receiving the gold bracelets which they were wearing?

HERCULES

DERIVATIONS

DERIVATIONS

1 Which islands take their name from the Latin for 'dog'?

2 What is the origin of the word trivial?

3 Which novelist coined the term nihilist and what does it mean?

4 What symbol of authority was adopted by Mussolini in 1919 and gives us the word fascism?

5 How may a somniloquist keep you awake?

6 In what would a lapidary be skilled?

7 What in English law are agnates and cognates?

8 Judging from the Latin

   (a) How many decades has a septuagenarian lived?

   (b) What happens if an army is decimated?

9 What may you hope to achieve with a placebo?

10 What would be the attraction of a sinecure?

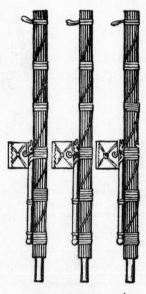

SEE QUESTION 4

22

11 Which Roman god gave his name to the month of January?

12 Name the form of writing, with wedge-shaped letters, used by the ancient Babylonians, Persians and Hittites.

13 What has a pinniped got instead of legs?

14 Which day of the week is named after a Roman god?

15 What do cruciverbalists fill in?

16 What does our word salary tell us about how a Roman soldier got paid?

17 When are matutinal duties carried out?

18 What would the earliest form of digital technology have involved?

19 What word which derives from the name of a Roman goddess is used to describe a woman who is big, buxom and beautiful?

DERIVATIONS

20 Homicide is the murder of a 'human being' (Latin *homo*). Who or what be would the victim of

(a) patricide

(b) sororicide

(c) tyrannicide

(d) regicide

(e) vulpicide?

SACRIFICIAL AXE

24

SCIENCE AND
NATURE

1 In astronomy what are the better known names for *Ursa Major* and *Ursa Minor*?

2 What Latin name is given to a star which suddenly flares up with explosive violence?

3 What Latin name is given to the group of alpine herbaceous perennial plants, which literally means 'stone breaker'?

4 What is the common name for the fruit *citrus sinensis*?

5 Give the Latin names for

(a) the two bones of the lower leg

(b) the two bones of the forearm

(c) the thigh bone.

6 What are the common names for the bones known in Latin as

(a) *sternum*

(b) *cranium*

(c) *scapula*.

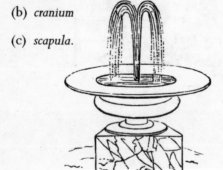

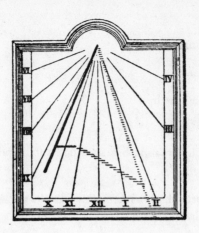

7 Is your *gluteus maximus* above or below your waist?

8 What and where is your *latissimus dorsi*?

9 By what name do gardeners more commonly refer to the plant *taraxacum officinale*?

10 Which flower has the Latin name *papaver somniferum*?

11 Give the meanings of the Latin words for these astrological signs

    (a) *Aquarius*   (c) *Cancer*

    (b) *Sagittarius*   (d) *Aries.*

12 What Latin words are these chemical symbols short for and what elements do they represent

    (a) Au   (c) Pb

    (b) Fe   (d) Sn?

13 Why are

   (a) incisors

   (b) molars

   (c) canine teeth

   so called?

14 Which tiny creature bears a long Latin name meaning 'cavedweller'?

15 Which branch of mathematics takes its name from the Latin word for 'pebble'?

16 What Latin name is given to a luminous concentration of gas and dust in space?

17 Which common infectious disease is named from the Latin word for 'red'?

18 What old measure of length, corresponding to about three miles, comes from the Late Latin word *leuga*?

19 To what part of the body does the prefix cerebro- refer?

20 What Latin names are given to cloud which is

   (a) at high altitude, thin and tuft-like

   (b) at medium altitude, puffy and white with a grey flat base

   (c) at low altitude, spreading across the whole sky, bringing persistent drizzling rain or mist at ground level?

ET TU BRUTE?

ROMANS IN

SHAKESPEARE

1 Which Shakespearean play is largely an adaptation of a
  Roman play by Plautus called *Menaechmi*, where humour
  arises from cases of mistaken identity?

2 (a) What fate do handmaidens Iras and Charmian share
      with their famous mistress?

  (b) In the same play, what is described as 'a burnish'd
      throne' which

      'Burn'd on the water; the poop was beaten gold,
      Purple the sails, and so perfumed that
      The winds were love-sick with them...'

3 (a) Which of Shakespeare's plays, based on the life of a
      historical character, portrays the tragedy which
      results from a clash of wills between a mother and
      her son's duty to his people?

  (b) Name the leading character's mother in this same
      play.

4 What striking anachronism is included in Shakespeare's *Julius Caesar*?

5 *In Julius Caesar*, who compares whom to a 'serpent's egg, which hatched would as his kind grow mischievous'?

6 According to the historians, Julius Caesar uttered the words 'You too, my child' in Greek as his assassins dealt their final blows. What famous words does Shakespeare have Julius Caesar say at this point?

7 In *Julius Caesar* who honours whom with the words 'This was a man'?

8 For which two plays was Shakespeare indebted to the Roman poet Ovid's telling of the story of Pyramus and Thisbe?

9 (a) Which play was based on the life of British king Cunobelinus, who befriended the Romans in the time of Emperor Augustus?

   (b) Name the main female character in this same play.

10 (a) In which play does Shakespeare make use of the *deus ex machina* device, by bringing a Roman god onstage?

   (b) Name the god.

WHERE
IN THE
ROMAN
WORLD?

IMP · CAESARI · DIVI · F
AVGVSTO
PONTIFICI · MAXIMO
COS · XIII · TRIB · POT · XXIII
PATRI · PATRIAE

1 On how many hills was Rome built?

2 Name at least four of them.

3 The ruined ancient city of Pompeii stands close to which volcano?

4 What was it that the ancient Romans called *mare nostrum*?

5 What region of modern France was called Gallia Narbonensis by the Romans?

6 Which were the first two islands to be made Roman provinces?

7 What was the name of the port which served Rome during the Empire?

8 In which hills does the river Tiber rise?

9 What was the name given by the Romans to

(a) Scotland

(b) Ireland?

10 Give the modern equivalents of the following Roman
    rivers

    (a) Rhenus

    (b) Danuvius

    (c) Tamesis

11 What is the modern name for the sea which the Romans
    called Pontus Euxinus?

12 What name was loosely applied to the large tract of land
    on the eastern side of the Adriatic sea, whose people
    were ancestors of the Albanians?

13 By what names did the Romans differentiate between the areas of Gaul which were

   (a) on the Italian side of the Alps

   (b) on the French side of the Alps?

14 What areas of Gaul were specified by the Roman use of the terms

   (a) Gallia Transpadana

   (b) Gallia Cispadana?

15 What was the name of the ancient Italian region which corresponds to modern day Tuscany, whose people, sometimes called *Tusci* by the Romans, were specially distinguished by their religious institutions?

16 What did the ancients call the Dardanelles?

17 As far as the Romans were concerned, where was Thule?

18 The Flaminian Way ran from Rome to where?

19 Give the name of the major city in Tunisia, which was destroyed utterly by the Romans in 146 BC but eventually colonised by Augustus and created capital of the province of Africa Proconsularis?

20 Name the city in the Roman province of Syria Phoenice, which was the seat of the famous purple-dying industry?

INSULT OR
FLATTERY?

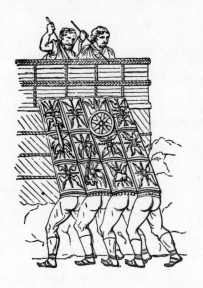

1 If someone said you were *ex hara productus*, would that make you

   (a) 'a product of a pig-pen' or

   (b) 'a product of an illustrious school of soothsayers'?

2 Does *cercopithecus* mean that you are

   (a) 'olive-skinned' or

   (b) 'monkey-featured'?

3 Would you like to be called *ocellus*? Does it mean that you

   (a) 'have piggy little eyes'

   (b) are the 'apple of someone's eye'?

4 How conscious are you of your figure? Would you prefer to be described as

   (a) the possessor of *planus venter* or

   (b) *ventriosus*?

5 As a *magnus ardelio* are you likely to be considered

   (a) 'a meddlesome busybody' or

   (b) 'a great lover'?

6 Does *venustus* mean that you have

(a) 'charm and beauty' or

(b) 'love for sale'?

7 As a good-looking young man, is it better to be regarded as
(a) *bellus* or

(b) *formosus*?

8 What is an *urbanus scurra* —
(a) 'the village idiot' or

(b) 'an elegant man about town?

9 If a lover called you *mea amoenitas*, would you be

(a) delighted to be someone's 'darling' or

(b) mortified at being someone's 'meal ticket'?

10 Would you like to be called a *pithecium*? Does it mean that you are

(a) 'calmness personified' or

(b) 'a little ape'?

11 Are you blessed or cursed with *tumentibus suris*, which may be

    (a) 'great fat calves' or

    (b) 'strong thighs'?

12 As a *voluptas* are you likely to be considered

    (a) 'a unique source of pleasure and delight' or

    (b) 'a voluptuary, someone excessively devoted to one's own pleasure'?

13 How might an *homunculus* be viewed –

    (a) as a 'dear, sweet little man' or

    (b) 'a pathetic excuse for a human being'?

14 Would a *spinturnicium* be a suitable love-token? Which would you prefer to receive –

    (a) 'a beautiful bracelet' or

    (b) 'a bird which will bring you bad luck'?

15 The term *deliciae* is always used in a loving context to refer to one's 'darling'. Is this

    (a) true or

    (b) false?

EVENTS IN
ROMAN
HISTORY

EVENTS IN ROMAN HISTORY

1 Give the full date of the assassination of Julius Caesar.

2 What city was destroyed by the Emperor Titus in AD 70 after a five month siege?

3 What event, which began on 19 June, AD 64 and lasted for nine days, proved devastating for Rome?

4 What honorific title was bestowed by the Senate on Octavian in 27 BC and what does it mean?

5 How did Octavian refer to himself, a title which gave rise to the term Principate to describe the rule of the Emperors?

6 What was the year of the founding of Rome according to the Roman scholar Varro?

7 According to the much-disputed legend, how many kings of Rome were there?

8 What year did Varro give for the end of Tyranny and the beginning of a new order called Republic?

9 What was the name of the list of statutes drawn up in 451/450 BC, which are considered to be the starting point from which the Roman legal system developed?

10 Of which Roman province in 73/71 BC was the Proconsul Verres tried and convicted of exploitation and oppression?

11 What is the name given to the official publication of the list of names of Roman citizens, which branded them as outlaws, who could expect at least to have their riches confiscated but were often also hunted down and killed?

12 Who murdered Clodius on 18 January, 52 BC as the climax to a sustained period of mob rioting and reprisals?

13 Which disappointed candidate for the Consulship of 63 BC was killed in battle soon after his co-conspirators were arrested and, amid much controversy, executed without trial for plotting against the state?

14 In AD 65 who hoped to become Emperor as the result of an attempted aristocratic plot to overthrow the Emperor Nero?

15 On what date did Vesuvius erupt, destroying Pompeii and the surrounding area?

16 What new document went on display in the Porticus Vipsania in Rome in the early days of Augustan Rome?

17 At the festival of the Lupercalia on 15 February, 44 BC, someone made a show of offering a royal diadem to Julius Caesar. Who was it?

18 Which Judaean fortress succumbed to defeat at the hands of the Romans after a six-month siege, when almost a thousand of its defenders committed suicide?

19 Which Greek historian and Jewish priest, who was eventually given Roman citizenship, wrote an account of the events of the so-called *Jewish War*?

20 Including the Eastern empire, how long did the Roman Empire survive?

BELIEFS AND
SUPERSTITIONS

1 What was the October Horse?

2 Who were the *Salii*?

3 In which festival was a pregnant cow sacrificed to Tellus (Earth)?

4 What Latin word did the Romans give to an action which was religiously permitted?

5 What title was given to the chief magistrate of the Roman religion?

6 What was the name of the festival which took place on 15 February, which involved so-called Wolf-men running naked through the city, striking bystanders with shaggy whips?

7 What was the *pomerium*?

8 What was the *genius* and how was it usually represented in Roman art?

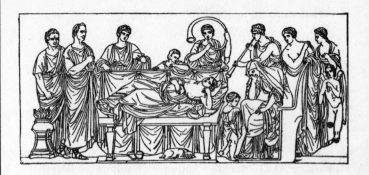

9 Which kind of priest was easily identifiable by his shaven head and white linen robes?

10 What popular cult involved brutal initiation rites — blindfolds, nakedness, swords etc. — a strict priestly pecking order, with titles such as Raven, Bride, Lion and Father, and may have originated in Persia?

11 Who or what was the *lamia*?

12 Which of these superstitions do we not inherit from the Romans

   (a) throwing coins into wishing wells

   (b) decoration of the house in December with holly

   (c) carrying a bride over the threshold

   (d) kissing under the mistletoe

   (e) touching wood?

13 What was augury and which early Roman king is believed to have made it an institution?

14 What were the special titles given to

   (a) the priest of Mars

   (b) the priest of Jupiter?

15 Who were the *penates*?

16 What was the *navigium Isidis*?

17 The following statements describe Roman rites of passage. Try to decide whether each statement is **true or false**.

   (a) May was considered a bad month to get married.

   (b) *deductio* was a common practice in the hills around Rome, whereby a man could simply carry off the wife of his choice.

   (c) People shouted obscenities about the dead man at his funeral and made loud and lewd remarks about a bridegroom's bachelor life during his wedding procession.

   (d) *sex crines* was the name given to an arrangement of lilies which adorned the hallway of a Roman house for six days prior to a wedding.

   (e) Within moments of someone dying, the person with him would shout his name as loudly as possible.

   (f) The Romans recognised Hallowe'en in their calendar.

18 Which one of the following was **not** considered bad luck by the Romans

(a) food falling from the hand of the chief priest during a ritual

(b) having your hair cut on board ship

(c) mentioning fire at a dinner party

(d) walking under a ladder

(e) allowing a black cat to enter your house

(f) meeting a mule carrying a load of herbs used to decorate tombs

(g) everyone falling silent at a dinner party when an odd number of guests is present

(h) an escaped bull climbing your stairs to the third floor

(i) a beam in your house splitting

(j) pickled fish beginning to wriggle around in a pan as if it is alive?

19 Would a Roman have written *arseverse* on his front door

   (a) to avoid the risk of fire, or

   (b) in celebration of the Saturnalia festival which includes a 'topsy-turvy day'?

20 The *taurobolium* was a sacred rite in honour of the Magna Mater, Cybele. Did it involve

   (a) a 'bull run' of the kind still seen today in the streets of Pamplona in Spain, or

   (b) a bull sacrifice, in which the warm blood of the beast was allowed to flow onto a worshipper and allow him to be 'born again'?

ROMAN EMPERORS

1 Who was Roman Emperor at the time of the Nativity?

2 Who was Roman Emperor at the time of the Crucifixion?

3 Which Roman emperor ruled from AD 117–38 and has a famous structure in the UK named after him?

4 Which Roman historian wrote an account of each of the lives of the so-called 'Twelve Caesars'?

5 Which was the year of the four emperors and what were their names?

6 What was the name of the month of August before it was renamed in honour of the Emperor Augustus?

7 Which ruthless Emperor executed at least twelve men of consular rank during a reign of terror, which was brought to a welcome end when he was allegedly killed by his closest friends and wife?

8 What blood relationship existed between the following pairs of Emperors

(a) Tiberius and Caligula

(b) Claudius and Nero

(c) Titus and Domitian

(d) Marcus Aurelius and Commodus?

9 Who had a famous Golden Palace built of legendary size and magnificence with a 30-metre-high statue of himself in the entrance hall?

10 Which Emperor was reported to have among his papers two books entitled *The Dagger* and *The Sword*, each of them containing names and addresses of men he planned to kill?

11 Under which Emperor was there a notoriously high incidence of trials before the Senate?

12 Which Emperor led the invasion of Britain in AD 43 and named his only son Britannicus?

13 Which of the so-called 'Twelve Caesars' were worshipped as gods?

14 To which Emperors were these notorious women married

(a) Poppaea

(b) Messalina

(c) Livia?

15 Which Emperor was assassinated on New Year's Eve AD 192, allegedly because he was planning to murder the incoming Consuls and half the Senate on New Year's Day AD 193?

16 Whose reign was tainted with allegations of decadent and immoral cavortings on the island of Capri?

17 Which Emperor added the country now known as Romania to the Empire?

18 Which Emperor was credited with making Christianity Rome's official religion?

19 Who is the only Roman Emperor to have a work published by Penguin?

20 Who was the last Roman Emperor of the West?

FOOD AND DINING

FOOD AND DINING

1 Do you think the following statements about food and dining in Rome are **true or false**:

(a) During a dinner party, a slave known as a *scissor* would cut up the guests' food.

(b) The Romans invented the use of the fork.

(c) Some guests used to bring their own napkin and take home in it the remains of their dinner, rather like a 'doggie bag'.

(d) The custom of reclining at dinner actually came from the ancient Greeks.

(e) It was quite acceptable to throw the remains of your dinner on the floor.

(f) The ancient Romans invented pizza.

(g) The Romans usually began their banquets at sunset, at the end of the 12th hour of the day.

(h) During the *comissatio* or 'after-dinner drinks', every guest put on a floral garland and lots of perfume.

(i) The Romans watered down their wine and drank it at room temperature or even slightly warmed.

(j) Orange and lemon groves were a common sight in the fertile area around the bay of Naples and the fruits were a staple of the Roman diet.

2 What would you expect to have been served at a Pompeian *thermopolium*?

3 What might you expect to find in a *gliraria*?

4 What was the main constituent of *garum* and how was it used?

5 What would a Roman keep in

(a) a *salinum*

(b) an *acetabulum*?

6 What meal did the Romans call
(a) *ientaculum*

(b) *prandium*?

7 What role might a *puer ad pedes* perform at a Roman banquet?

FOOD AND DINING

8 Which one of the following birds was not eaten by the ancient Romans

(a) swan   (f) stork

(b) peacock   (g) thrush

(c) chicken   (h) parrot

(d) ostrich   (i) lark

(e) flamingo   (j) turkey?

9 Which one of the following fruits did the Romans not enjoy

(a) apple   (f) grape

(b) pear   (g) quince

(c) banana   (h) apricot

(d) plum   (i) date

(e) cherry   (j) fig?

10 What was *secunda mensa*?

LITERATURE

1 Which Roman poet was the author of at least a dozen epigrams, published in AD 80?

2 Who wrote *The Golden Ass*, the only Latin novel which has survived intact?

3 Which notorious connoisseur of luxury – especially in food – is believed to have made the collection of recipes which is known to us as the *Roman Cookery Book*?

4 Shakespeare's poem *The Rape of Lucrece* was based on the poet Ovid's narrative in his *Fasti* of the famous story from Rome's past. Which Roman historian also tells the tale in his *Ab Urbe Condita*?

5 Which Roman poet wrote a poem which had poetry as its central theme?

6 Which writer of the fragmentary novel *Satyrica* may have been a politician and courtier of the Emperor Nero who was forced to commit suicide in AD 66?

7 (a) Who was the Roman architect who served as a military engineer for Julius Caesar and wrote an influential treatise on architecture and engineering called *De Architectura*?

(b) Which Roman governor of Britain, who established the

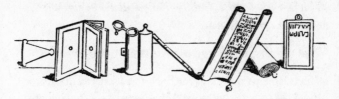

fortress at Caerleon in south Wales, wrote a treatise on the history, administration and maintenance of Rome's aqueducts?

8 Which comic playwright of Rome wrote six plays, all of which are extant, the most famous of which are *The Eunuch* and *The Brothers*?

9 Who are the Roman poets who name the following mistresses in their poems

(a) Lesbia

(b) Corinna

(c) Cynthia

(d) Delia?

10 Which poet wrote short lyrics and epigrams which were influenced by the neat elegance of Hellenistic Greek poems and surrounded himself with a group of young, like-minded writers known as 'Neoterics'?

11 What was the name of the major poetic work of Lucretius, which was allegedly written in short spells of sanity after he was driven mad by a love potion which had been administered by his wife?

12 Which work begins, *Gallia est omnis divisa in partes tres*, and what does it mean?

13 What did the poet Virgil ask for as his dying wish?

14 Which Roman poet was author of at least twenty tragic plays based on Greek models but was better known for his narrative poem on the history of the Roman people, the *Annales*?

15 Which prolific and versatile Roman writer, whose most important works were his tragedies, suffered a tragic fate of his own when he was forced to commit suicide in AD 65 for his supposed collaboration in the unsuccessful plot to overthrow Nero?

16 Which Roman poet wrote, amongst other works, three books of elegies on the subject of his own love affairs and went on to use his experiences for a didactic poem on the art of courtship?

17 Which play by Plautus was the source of Molière's *L'Avare*?

18 Which Roman historian's major works were *The Histories* and *The Annals*?

19 Who was the author of an autobiographical poem called *Consulatus Suus* and an epic on the subject of Gaius Marius but, thankfully, did not give up the day job to concentrate on poetry?

20 Name the thirty-seven book encyclopaedia which was painstakingly researched and written by Pliny the Elder.

LATIN IN USE TODAY

1 Give the full Latin version of the following abbreviations and say what each one means

   (a) i.e.   (f) p.p.

   (b) e.g.   (g) n.b.

   (c) p.a.   (h) R.I.P.

   (d) Q.E.D.   (i) A.D.

   (e) P.S.   (j) c.v.

2 What is the modern equivalent of the following Roman numerals

   (a) CXL   (c) LXVI

   (b) MD   (d) MCM

3 What is the meaning of the phrases

   (a) *ad hoc*   (b) *ad infinitum*?

4 Which Latin phrases commonly used in English law literally mean

   (a) 'while the crime is still blazing' or 'caught red-handed'

   (b) 'you may have the body'?

5 If a meeting adjourns *sine die*, when will it reconvene?

6 Give the full Latin word or phrase for each of the following abbreviations and say what each one means

(a) viz.

(f) pro/con.

(b) sc.

(g) vox pop.

(c) etc.

(h) ibid.

(d) ad lib.

(i) cf.

(e) et al.

(j) loc. cit.

7 What name is given to a language, usually a hybrid one, which is used as a means of communication between different peoples?

8 With what Latin phrase did Queen Elizabeth II sum up the year 1992?

9 Why may an item in a shop be labelled *caveat emptor*?

10 Which organisations have these mottoes and what do they mean

(a) *per mare per terram*

(b) *per ardua ad astra*

(c) *citius altius fortius*

(d) *arts gratia artis*?

11 What is the role of

   (a) a *locum tenens*

   (b) one who is *in loco parentis*?

12 Give the Latin phrase which means 'with a clean slate'?

13 How is 'word for word' expressed in Latin?

14 Give the Latin phrase which means 'God willing'?

15 What is the Latin phrase for 'being of sound mind'?

16 What is distinctive about a *viva voce* examination?

17 If a reference is *passim*, where would you find it?

18 If something is *gratis*, how much would it cost you?

19 What does it mean when something is *bona fide*?

20 How could something be rendered *vice versa*?

ART AND
ARCHITECTURE

1 Why is Rome's largest amphitheatre called the Colosseum

   (a) because of its colossal size

   (b) because it was built by prisoners from Colossus

   (c) because it was built next to a colossal statue of Nero?

2 Which of the following is **not** the name of part of a Roman house

   (a) *tablinum*

   (b) *atrium*

   (c) *peculium*

   (d) *peristylium*?

3 What artistically speaking links the *exedra* of the House of the Faun in Pompeii, the Sanctuary of Fortuna at Praeneste (Palestrina) and the fourth-century villa at Piazza Amerina in Sicily?

4 Near which British city would you find the Fishbourne villa?

5 The earliest permanent theatre in Rome was named after which politician of the first century BC?

6 Which plant's leaves decorate the capital of a Corinthian column?

SEE
QUESTION 6

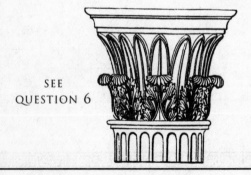

7 Which common public building used by the Romans gave its shape to the earliest Christian churches?

8 In which building of public entertainment would you have found the *carceres, metae* and *spina*?

9 In the remains of which ancient building did the so-called Three Tenors give their first World Cup 1990 concert?

10 Which of these buildings of entertainment in Rome had the largest seating capacity

(a) the Theatre of Marcellus

(b) the Flavian Amphitheatre (Colosseum)

(c) the Circus Maximus?

11 Where in Rome can you see a sculpture 200 metres long, commemorating the defeat of the Dacians by the Roman army in the first decade of the second century AD?

12 In which ancient building in Rome are the kings of modern Italy buried?

13 The Romans did not have glass for their windows: true or false?

14 Why according to the Romans themselves were temples of the goddess Vesta invariably round?

15 What is the name of the monumental altar dedicated by Augustus and decorated with sculpted panels and friezes of a procession which includes Augustus himself?

16 One of the best preserved of all ancient temples is in the French city of Nîmes. What is it called today?

17 What links the following buildings

    (a) John Nash's original entrance to Buckingham Palace, designed in 1827

    (b) the central feature of the Place Charles de Gaulle in Paris

    (c) Stanford White's commemoration of the centenary of George Washington's inauguration in Washington Square, New York city?

18 Which Emperor's bronze equestrian statue stood for many years on a pedestal in the centre of the Campidoglio in Rome?

19 Which colour, prominent on the walls of the houses of Pompeii, has earned an entry in the Oxford English Dictionary?

20 What object in the British Museum in London is considered by many to be an outstanding example of ancient Roman cameo work?

WHAT DOES IT
REALLY MEAN?

Choose the correct translation for the following Latin phrases. Watch out for the 'howlers'!

1 *sic transit gloria mundi*

  (a) Gloria was ill on the boat on Monday
  (b) look for a vehicle
  (c) that's how the world's glory passes

2 *Ariadne gladium ei dedit*

  (a) Ariadne gave him a sword
  (b) Ariadne dedicated her eye
  (c) Ariadne gave him the glad eye

3 *Caesar, secundum ventum nactus*

  (a) Caesar, trying to get wind of his fortunate circumstances
  (b) Caesar, having chanced upon a favourable wind
  (c) Caesar, having got his second wind

4 *Ave, Domine*

  (a) Lord, I am a bird
  (b) Hail, O Lord
  (c) the Lord is my light

5 *in loco parentis*

  (a) in the place of a parent
  (b) following in a parent's footstep's
  (c) my parents are mad

6 *ne plus ultra*

  (a) no more for you
  (b) nothing beyond it
  (c) nothing beyond Ulster

7 LXXX

  (a) love and kisses

  (b) 130

  (c) 80

8 *Anno Domini*

  (a) after death

  (b) in the year of our Lord

  (c) the Lord's my shepherd

9 *de gustibus non est disputandum*

  (a) there's no accounting for tastes

  (b) high winds and no mistake

  (c) a judge of good taste

10 *infra dig.*

  (a) terrible lodgings

  (b) beneath one's dignity

  (c) dig down here

11 *prima facie*

  (a) prime location

  (b) original complexion

  (c) at first sight

12 *te deum*

  (a) two to you

  (b) thee o God

  (c) today's the day

13 *dum spiro spero*

  (a) stupid Greek person, I presume

  (b) as the world turns

  (c) where there's life, there's hope

14 *de mortuis nil nisi bonum*

  (a) (say) nothing but good about the dead

  (b) in the dead there's nothing but bones

  (c) the omens are favourable

15 *caveat emptor*

  (a) look out, it's empty

  (b) beware of pot-holes

  (c) let the buyer beware

16 *festina lente*

  (a) more haste, less speed

  (b) the festival of Lent

  (c) fasten your seat-belts

17 *canes domuum custodes sunt*
   (a) canes are the guardians of the masters
   (b) dogs are the guardians of houses
   (c) a key unlocks the holy doors

18 *nota bene*
   (a) note well
   (b) not a penny
   (c) a well-known benefactor

19 *receptui canere*
   (a) to sing at a reception
   (b) to sound the retreat
   (c) to turn grey under pressure

20 *pueri pauperum misereri discite*
   (a) poor miserable boys, you must learn
   (b) miserable boys are poor learners
   (c) boys, learn to have compassion for the poor

ROME IN THE MOVIES

1 One of the greatest true stories of the ancient world ever to hit the big screen was adapted from a novel by Howard Fast and released in 1960. What was it?

2 Peter Ustinov won Academy Awards for two films with Roman subjects. Name the role and the film for which he won

(a) the award for Best Actor

(b) the award for Best Supporting Actor.

3 Which sultry and statuesque actress was an extra — along with her mother — in 1951's *Quo Vadis* and went on to play Lucilla in *The Fall of the Roman Empire* in 1964?

4 (a) Which film with a Roman theme swept the board at the 1959 Academy Awards, winning Best Picture as well as Best Cinematography, Editing, Score, Art Direction, Costume Design and Visual Effects?

(b) Can you also name the individual winners of this same film's Best Director, Best Actor and Best Supporting Actor?

5 (a) Who was nominated in 1953 for an Academy Award for his portrayal in *The Robe* of Military Tribune Marcellus Gallio?

(b) Name the sequel which was spawned by this film.

(c) Which role did Victor Mature play in both films?

6 (a) Jay Robinson put in a fine, flamboyant turn as Caligula in *The Robe*. Who played the insanely cruel Emperor in *Caligula* in 1977?

(b) What part did Peter O'Toole play in the same film?

7 Who played Julius Caesar in the following films

(a) *Cleopatra* (1934)

(b) *Cleopatra* (1963)

(c) *Caesar and Cleopatra* (1945)

(d) *Julius Caesar* (1953)

(e) *Carry On Cleo* (1964)?

8 Who was the Producer and Director of *Cleopatra* (1934) and was famous for his obsession with authentic detail and lavish spectacle?

9 Which actor had a talent for portraying Roman Emperors, playing Nero in *The Sign of the Cross* (1932) and the eponymous role in the unfinished *I Claudius* (1937)?

10 Which film set in ancient Rome earned an Academy Award nomination for Best Director, Federico Fellini, in 1969, and was based on a fragmentary novella by Gaius Petronius?

11 Which actor was well-suited to the roles of evil but sexy villains such as Messala in *Ben-Hur* and Livius in *The Fall of the Roman Empire*?

12 Who played Cleopatra in the following movies:

(a) *Cleopatra* (1934)

(b) *Cleopatra* (1963)

(c) *Caesar and Cleopatra* (1945)

(d) *Carry On Cleo* (1964)?

13 (a) Which film musical of 1966 was based on several comic plays of Plautus?

(b) Who directed it?

(c) Which actor played the Roman slave Pseudolus?

14 The Roman prefect of Judaea at the time of the Crucifixion, Pontius Pilate, not surprisingly features in several biblical epics. Who played the role in

(a) *The Last Days of Pompeii* (1935)

(b) *The Greatest Story Ever Told*

(c) *The Passover Plot*?

15 What roles did

(a) Sir Alec Guinness, and

(b) Christopher Plummer play in *The Fall of the Roman Empire* (1964)?

16 Who played Mark Antony in

(a) *Cleopatra* (1934)

(b) *Cleopatra* (1963)

(c) *Julius Caesar* (1970)

(d) *Carry On Cleo* (1964)?

17 What Latin message is Brian told to paint on the walls in *The Life of Brian* and what does it mean?

18 Which movie set in Roman times was the most expensive silent film ever made?

19 Which 1951 film required a record-breaking wardrobe of 32,000 costumes?

20 For which great Hollywood epic of the ancient world was an almost full sized Roman Forum built on set?

ROMANS
AT WAR

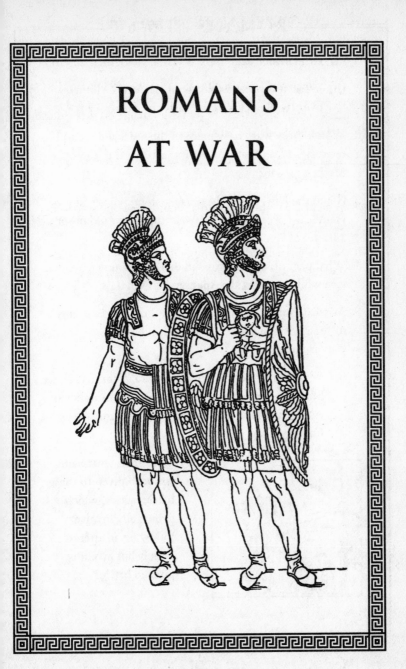

1 (a) After which king were 'Pyrrhic victories' named?

  (b) What was remarkable about this king's victories over the Romans in the early third century BC?

2 Which three wars took place in the third and second centuries BC against Rome's imperial rival in the Mediterranean?

3 Name the famous Carthaginian general whose father Hamilcar Barca made him swear that he would never be a friend of Rome?

4 What part of his anatomy did this Carthaginian general lose while crossing the Apennine hills in 217 BC?

5 At what famous battle in 216 BC did the Roman army suffer a devastating defeat at the hands of the Carthaginians?

6 (a) What name did the Roman general Quintus Fabius Maximus Verrucosus earn for his famous policy of attrition, which made final victory against the Carthaginians possible?

  (b) Since then what name has been given to these battle tactics, which principally involve following an enemy closely but avoiding pitched battle?

7 Which general triumphed at the battle of Zama in 202 BC and what title did he earn as a result?

8 Which successful commander, who held an unprecedented series of Consulships, undertook to reform the system of recruitment to the Roman army in the early part of the first century BC?

9 Which successful Roman general marched on Rome and got himself pronounced Dictator in 80 BC whilst Julius Caesar was still a young man?

10 Who was Rome's enemy in the so-called Social War of 91–87 BC?

11 Who enjoyed a magnificent triumph in 62 BC after defeating Mithradates VI of Pontus and completely reorganising Rome's eastern provinces?

12 Near what northern Mesopotamian city was the Roman general and Triumvir Crassus defeated in 53 BC?

13 What war was fought between the years of 58–51 BC and who was in special command of the Roman forces at the time?

14 Which two generals fought a decisive duel in 52 BC, which led to the siege of Alesia and the annexation of Gaul?

15 At what battle did Julius Caesar defeat Pompey in 48 BC?

16 Philippi in eastern Macedonia was the site of two important battles in 42 BC.

(a) Name the two generals who were victorious.

(b) Name the two generals who were defeated and committed suicide.

17 In what famous sea battle were Mark Antony and the Egyptian queen Cleopatra defeated by Octavian in 31 BC?

18 Which temple's gates were opened in time of war and closed in time of peace and were allegedly closed only three times in a period of 700 years of Rome's turbulent history?

19 Which Roman general in the Rhine in AD 9 committed suicide when his three legions were annihilated by German forces led by someone he had considered to be an ally?

20 Which Emperor allegedly drew up his army in battle array on the beach and then ordered his soldiers to collect shells as plunder from his triumph over the sea?

ANSWERS

1 Julian 'the Apostate' (Emperor AD 361–3) was referring to Jesus, after trying unsuccessfully to turn the Empire against Christianity.

2 King Pyrrhus of Epirus, who had in that victorious battle suffered great slaughter of his own side, and gave his name to a 'Pyrrhic victory'.

3 The poet Virgil put these words into the mouth of a Trojan who was – rightly – suspicious of the wooden horse which the Greeks appeared to have left for them (*Aeneid* II.49).

4 Cicero was defending Milo for the murder of Clodius and was asking 'who stood to gain' from Clodius' death. Interestingly, the speech (*Pro Milone*) was never delivered in court but was published by Cicero after Milo's conviction and exile.

5 Horace (*Odes* III.ii.13)

6 (a) 'The die is cast.'
   (b) Julius Caesar at the crossing of the river Rubicon, an act which precipitated civil war and gave rise to our own still-used saying.

7 St Augustine (*Confessions* VIII.7)

8 The Emperor Augustus

9 The poet Juvenal asked 'Who will guard the guards themselves?' (*Satires* VI.347–8)

10 The Emperor Nero, who was an enthusiastic performer and lover of all things Greek.

11 The poet Propertius, referring to the *Aeneid* of Virgil (*Elegies* XXXIV.65).

12 Horace, referring to the way in which Greek culture continued to captivate the Romans many years after the annexation of Greece. The 'rough' Romans had little culture of their own until they started to be inspired by and imitate their Greek captives (*Epistles* II.i.156).

13 The poet Juvenal wanted only 'a sound mind in a sound body' (*Satires* X.356).

14 (a) 'I came, I saw, I conquered.'
   (b) Julius Caesar used this snappy phrase to indicate the speed and efficiency with which he had concluded his Pontic campaign of 47 BC. Suetonius tells us that these words were inscribed onto the side of a decorated wagon in the triumphant procession; Plutarch has the victorious general write them in a letter. Either way, this has to be the best known quotation from Roman history.

15 Cato the Censor. It means 'Carthage must be destroyed', which it ultimately was in 146 BC.

16 (a) 'Oh what times, oh what habits!'
   (b) Cicero was bemoaning the state of affairs which led to the so-called Catilinarian conspiracy of 63 BC (*In Catilinam* I.i.1).

17 The Emperor Augustus. Varus had lost three legions in the Rhine in AD 9. The defeat had a profound effect on Augustus and many felt that his regime never quite recovered from the shock.

18 (a) 'What a fine artist dies with me!'
   (b) The Emperor Nero.

19 Caligula, expressing his desire to kill the lot of them in one fell swoop.

20 Horace – they mean 'now is the moment for a drink' and 'live for the day'.

1 Domestic dog

2 Polar bear

3 Their teeth are unusual or absent.

4 They are hoofed animals.

5 *Genus* and *species*

6 Pigs

7 *Cave canem*, meaning 'Beware of the dog'.

8 Incitatus – whose owner was Caligula.

9 (a) One who eats (Latin *voro*) vegetation (*herba*)

   (b) A meat-eater (*caro, carnis*)

   (c) One who eats everything (*omnis*)

10 (a) Ants (*formica*)

   (b) Birds (*avis*)

   (c) Bees (*apis*)

11 (a) Cattle (Latin *bos*)

   (b) Sheep (*ovis*)

   (c) Dog (*canis*)

(d) Cat (*feles*)

(e) Eagle (*aquila*)

(f) Horse (*equus*)

(g) Fox (*vulpis*)

(h) Lion (*leo*)

12 Onager

13 Reptiles (*reptilis*, from *repere*, 'creep')

14 Insects (*inseco* 'cut')

15 The cat's whiskers

16 It would take far less than this Black Widow Spider to make someone who was scared of spiders run away.

17 Pig (Latin *sus*), sheep (*ovis*) and bull (*taurus*)

18 A she-wolf

19 Geese

20 The Eagle (*Aquila*) was the symbol on the standard which was carried into battle.

THE ROMANS
IN BRITAIN
(ANSWERS TO PAGES 9–12)

1 A Roman fort on Hadrian's Wall

2 The Forth and the Clyde

3 (a) York
   (b) Colchester

4 (a) Deal in Kent
   (b) Richborough in Kent

5 Newcastle and Carlisle

6 (a) Aquae Sulis
   (b) Deva

7 The Iceni in East Anglia

8 Suetonius Paulinus

9 Watling Street

10 (a) Mona
   (b) Vectis

11 *Legio IX* (The Ninth)

12 (a) London, near Westminster Bridge
   (b) Under platform 10 (suburban line) at King's Cross Station (unconfirmed!)

13 Londinium and Lindum (London and Lincoln)

14 Caerleon, known as Isca Silurum to the Romans

15 (a) *Augusta*
   (b) *Valeria Victrix*

16 This is a popular belief in the town of Fortingall on Tayside.

17 (a) Togodubnus
   (b) Caractacus. The Emperor Claudius was persuaded by his eloquence to spare his life.

18 Septimius Severus (died AD 211) and Constantius I (died AD 306)

19 Cambridge

20 (a) Tacitus, his son-in-law
   (b) The battle of Mons Graupius

FAMOUS ROMANS

(ANSWERS TO PAGES 13–16)

1 Three – Cornelia, Pompeia, Calpurnia

2 Ovid. The reasons given were the naughty but nice poem *Ars Amatoria* and the poet's supposed involvement in an 'indiscretion'. Sadly, he was never recalled and died in exile.

3 King Mausolus ruled for a time in Halicarnassus in modern Turkey. Nothing is exciting about his life except the construction of his tomb, which was one of the Seven Wonders of the Ancient World. Construction may have started during the king's lifetime and was completed around 350 BC, three years after his death. Only the foundation now remains.

4 Caesar, Pompey, Crassus

5 Mark Antony, Octavian, Lepidus

6 Julius Caesar linked the year to the course of the sun and realised the need for the addition of an entire day every fourth year. His calendar continued to be used until 1582.

7 Arria the Elder. The occasion was the condemnation and ultimate suicide of her husband Caecina Paetus for his part in a conspiracy against the Emperor Claudius.

8 Caesarion. She also had three children by Mark Antony.

9 Pliny the Elder, firstly out of curiosity and then as part of a serious rescue mission, had sailed from Misenum right into the volcano's danger zone with fatal consequences. He died after inhaling fumes at Stabiae, a town just down the coast from Pompeii. A famous description of the event is given by his nephew, Pliny the Younger.

10 Sejanus. His successor Macro helped Tiberius to have him tried and executed for conspiracy.

11 The poet Virgil. The last part neatly sums up Virgil's three major works: the 'pastures' refers to his *Eclogues* or 'pastoral' poetry; 'fields' or more specifically agriculture is the subject of his *Georgics* and 'kings' played a leading role in his epic, *The Aeneid*.

12 Pandateria, but she was moved to Rhegium six years later. Augustus was appalled by his daughter's misbehaviour at a time when he was trying so hard to promote his as the model family. Her daughter, also called Julia, soon afterwards shared a similar fate for the same offence.

13 Clodius. Cicero was prosecuting counsel but Clodius got off, allegedly by bribing the jury.

14 Spartacus. The army was crushed and any survivors were crucified by Crassus.

15 The Censor (*Censorius*). Censor was the title given to one of a pair of senior Roman magistrates who were in charge of the census but also had the authority to supervise the morals of the community and blacklist reprehensible individuals.

16 Horace. He met his patron Maecenas, Octavian's right-hand man at Philippi, in 38 BC and was soon afterwards introduced to the man himself.

17 Pliny the Younger. His tenth book of letters features both sides of the regular correspondence between Pliny and the Emperor.

18 Atticus. Cicero's *Letters to Atticus* were published in one volume some time in the first century AD.

19 Clodia, sister of Clodius. A colourful presence in the social circles of the day, she was married at the time to Metellus, whom – if we believe Cicero – she probably murdered. Her tempestuous love affair with Catullus inspired some of his best poems.

20 Uncle and nephew, though the former brought up the latter.

MYTH AND LEGEND

(ANSWERS TO PAGES 17–20)

1 Bacchus was the Roman equivalent of the Greek god Dionysus.

2 Fire

3 (a) Mercury, the patron god of circulation, communication and commerce
  (b) Vesta, goddess of the hearth, whose cult in Rome was believed to guarantee the city's permanence
  (c) Neptune, god of the sea
  (d) Cupid, god of desire, sometimes known as Amor, the son and constant companion of his mother Venus
  (e) Jupiter, king of the heavens and earth
  (f) Diana, goddess of the moon, hunting and female rites of passage

4 Pluto, god of the underworld

5 Aurora, whom the Greeks called Eos

6 (a) Maia
  (b) Latona (Greek name Leto)

7 Venus, goddess of love and beauty, became associated with the Greek goddess Aphrodite, who was believed to have been born from the severed genitals of Uranus. This may have taken place on the coast of Cyprus. In any case, Cyprus was the home of her most famous cults, which explains her title.

8 Hercules

9 Ulysses

10 Cyclopes. The poet Virgil also has them assisting Vulcan in his forge within Etna, a volcano on Sicily.

11 Pygmalion. The story is told in the poet Ovid's *Metamorphoses* and has been used to comic effect in Shaw's play *Pygmalion* and Gilbert's 'three act fairy comedy' *Pygmalion and Galatea*.

12 Saturn was an early Roman deity sometimes erroneously associated with the Greek god Cronos. His festival, or Saturnalia, was held on 17 December.

13 Fauns. The god of fields and shepherds, Faunus, was the Roman equivalent of the Greek god Pan.

14 Sibyls. The most celebrated was the Sibyl of Cumae who was consulted by the legendary Trojan hero Aeneas before he descended to the Underworld.

15 The god Mars and the Vestal Virgin Rhea Silvia

16 The Sabine women, from the hills to the north of Rome, came to a festival and were sitting ducks for the eager Romans who had hitherto been unable to attract female companions.

17 Quirinus. To the Romans he was the third great god after Jupiter and his father Mars.

18 Horatius Cocles. When their task was nearly finished, Horatius sent his two companions back and, as the bridge fell, he plunged into the Tiber fully armed and safely swam to the opposite bank to a hero's welcome. The story is related in Macaulay's *Lays of Ancient Rome*.

19 The Horatius brothers. Only one Horatius survived the fight but he went on to destroy Alba Longa and bring its inhabitants under the dominion of Rome.

20 The treacherous Tarpeia was actually killed by the soldiers she tried to help. When she asked them for what they were wearing on their arms, she hardly expected them to weigh her down with their shields and crush her to death. She was buried under a precipitous aspect of the Capitoline hill which took her name. From that day, the Romans thought it fitting to throw traitors over the Tarpeian rock.

DERIVATIONS

(ANSWERS TO PAGES 21–24)

1 The Canary Islands (*canis*)

2 From the Latin word *trivium* meaning 'the junction of three roads' therefore 'common or garden'.

3 Turgenev. A nihilist is someone who believes that nothing (Latin *nihil*) has real existence.

4 The *fasces* were bundles of elm or birch rods tied together with an axe, and carried by lictors.

5 By talking (*loqui*)in his/her sleep (*somnus*)

6 The cutting, polishing and engraving of gemstones (*lapides*)

7 Agnates are the relations on your father's side, cognates are on your mother's side (*agnatus/cognatus*).

8 (a) seven, from *septem*

    (b) every tenth man is killed, from *decem*

9 A placebo is designed to keep a patient happy (*placeo*) rather than have any direct medicinal effect.

10 A sinecure is task which requires no effort (*sine cura*).

11 Janus, god of doors. All passages and beginnings were under his care.

12 Cuneiform (Latin *cuneus*, 'wedge')

13 Flippers (literally 'winged feet' from the Latin *pinnis/pedes*)

14 Saturn gave his name to Saturday.

15 Crosswords (*crux, crucis/verba*)

16 *Salarium* was the quantity of salt with which a Roman soldier was paid. It was then a very valuable commodity.

17 In the morning (*matutinus*)

18 Counting on the fingers (Latin *digiti*)

19 Junoesque

20 (a) Father (*pater, patris*)   (b) Sister (*soror, sororis*)

    (c) and (d) are both kings, from *tyrannus, tyranni* and *rex, regis*

    (e) Foxes (*vulpes, vulpis*)

SCIENCE AND NATURE

(ANSWERS TO PAGES 25–28)

1 Great Bear and Little Bear constellations

2 Nova. This is short for *nova stella* which means 'new star'.

3 *saxifraga* are so called because their roots 'break up rocks' by growing into cracks.

4 Orange (literally 'Chinese citrus')

5 (a) *tibia* and *fibula*
(b) *radius* and *ulna*
(c) *femur*

6 (a) Breast-bone
(b) Skull
(c) Shoulder-blade

7 Below. It is the muscle which forms the buttock.

8 It is one of two muscles which run across your back.

9 Dandelion

10 Opium Poppy

11 (a) Water-carrier
(b) Archer
(c) Crab
(d) Ram

12 (a) *aurum* or gold
(b) *ferrum* or iron
(c) *plumbum* or lead
(d) *stannum* or tin

13 (a) Incisors 'cut into' food (Latin *incido*).
(b) Molars 'grind' it up (*molo*).
(c) Canine teeth resemble the fangs of dogs (*canis*).

14 The wren is *Troglodytes*.

15 Calculus

16 Nebula (Latin for 'dust')

17 Rubella (or German measles)

18 League

19 Brain (Latin *cerebrum*)

20 (a) Cirrus (Latin for 'tuft')
(b) Cumulus (Latin for 'mass')
(c) Stratus (Latin for 'covering')

ET TU BRUTE?
ROMANS IN SHAKESPEARE
(ANSWERS TO PAGES 29–32)

1 *The Comedy of Errors*. Plautus has just one set of twins – the Menaechmus brothers of the title – whilst Shakespeare ambitiously uses two Dromios and two Antipholuses!

2 (a) Cleopatra died at her own hand by the bite of a royal asp soon after Octavian captured Alexandria in 30 BC. Shakespeare faithfully portrays the death scene in *Antony and Cleopatra*, with pathos enhanced by the companionable suicide of her handmaidens.
  (b) Cleopatra's barge

3 (a) *Coriolanus*, which means 'citizen of Corioli', a title which the main character Gaius Marcius earns during the course of the play.
  (b) Volumnia

4 In Act II, scene 1, the 'clock hath stricken three'.

5 Brutus is speaking of Julius Caesar.

6 '*Et tu, Brute?* Then fall, Caesar.'

7 Antony is speaking of Brutus, who has just committed suicide following a humiliating defeat at the battle of Philippi.

8 *A Midsummer Night's Dream* contains a comic rendition of the story. *Romeo and Juliet* share the lovers' tragic fate.

9 (a) *Cymbeline*
  (b) Imogen, his daughter

10 (a) *Cymbeline*
  (b) Jupiter

WHERE IN THE
ROMAN WORLD?
(ANSWERS TO PAGES 33–36)

1 Seven

2 Aventine, Caelian, Capitoline, Esquiline, Palatine, Quirinal,
   Viminal

3 Vesuvius

4 The Mediterranean – literally 'our sea' – a term which was
   adopted by Mussolini

5 Provence

6 Sicily and Sardinia

7 Ostia

8 The Apennines

9 (a) Caledonia
   (b) Hibernia

10 (a) Rhine
   (b) Danube
   (c) Thames

11 The Black Sea

12 Illyria

13 (a) Gallia Cisalpina
   (b) Gallia Transalpina

14 (a) on the other side of the river Po, which the Romans
        called Padanus
   (b) on the Italian side of the river Po

15 Etruria. Its people are more often known as Etruscans.

16 The Hellespont

17 It was the most northerly land they knew, about six days' sail
   to the north of Britain and could have been Iceland or
   Norway. Ultima Thule became proverbial amongst the
   Romans for the furthest place on earth.

WHERE IN THE
ROMAN WORLD?
(ANSWERS TO PAGES 33–36)

18 Ariminum, which is modern day Rimini

19 Carthage was razed to the ground by the Romans on the
    instruction of Cato the Censor as the final, triumphant act of
    three long wars against the Carthaginians. The city was
    rebuilt and colonised by Augustus, created capital of the
    province of Africa Proconsularis and eventually became
    second only to Rome in the western Mediterranean.
    Carthage is perhaps most famous for its legendary queen,
    Dido, whose passionate – but ultimately tragic – liaison with
    Aeneas, the future founder of the Roman race, has been
    widely celebrated in art, literature and music.

20 Tyre. Roman Senators wore togas which were bordered with
    Tyrian purple, a dye obtained from shellfish. The colour was a
    mark of high rank.

INSULT OR FLATTERY?

(ANSWERS TO PAGES 37–40)

1 *ex hara productus* is a 'product of a pig-pen'.

2 *cercopithecus* means 'monkey-featured'.

3 *ocellus* literally means 'little eye' but is usually rendered 'apple of one's eye' since it is always a term of endearment.

4 *planus venter* means 'flat belly'; *ventriosus* means 'fat-bellied'.

5 *magnus ardelio* means 'a meddlesome busybody'.

6 *venustus* means 'charming' or 'beautiful'.

7 Both *bellus* and *formosus* mean 'handsome', but *bellus* implies that the young man is a 'pretty boy' in an unkind context.

8 *urbanus scurra* means 'the village idiot' as a phrase, though the words individually mean 'elegant' and 'gentleman'.

9 *amoenitas* gives us the word 'amenity' which may suggest a means to an end but was in ancient times always used as a flattering term such as 'my darling'.

10 *pithecium* is a 'little ape'.

11 *tumentibus suris* are 'great fat calves'.

12 *voluptas* means 'darling' or literally 'my source of pleasure'

13 Although the diminutive ending -ulus sounds endearing, *homunculus* means 'pathetic excuse for a human being' and is never a flattering term.

14 *spinturnicium* is a 'bird of ill omen'.

15 False: *deliciae* can also be used scathingly of a 'parasite' or 'minion'.

EVENTS IN
ROMAN HISTORY
(ANSWERS TO PAGES 41–44)

1 The Ides or 15 March, 44 BC

2 Jerusalem

3 The great fire of Rome. Rumours abounded that the Emperor Nero not only started the fire but recited his own poems over the blazing city. Nero for his part blamed the Christians and had a large number of them burned alive as a suitable punishment.

4 *Augustus* or 'revered one'

5 *Princeps inter pares* or 'first among equals'

6 753 BC, though evidence suggests that Varro got it wrong. The city walls were not erected until *c*378 BC although there is evidence of settlement as far back as the ninth century BC.

7 Seven. Their names were Romulus, Numa Pompilius, Tullius Hostilius, Ancus Marcius, Tarquinius Priscus, Servius Tullius and Tarquinius Superbus. In 250 years of Tyranny, there must have been more than seven kings, so Varro certainly got either the dates or his numbers wrong!

8 509 BC, which is probably quite near the mark. The last king was expelled in an aristocratic coup led by an ancestor of '*et tu*' Brutus; from that time two annually elected consuls held power instead.

9 The Twelve Tables

10 Sicily. Cicero's prosecuting *Verrine Orations* give an excellent insight into the potential for abuse of the provincial administrative system.

11 Proscription. Sulla was believed to have eliminated over five hundred of his political opponents in this way in 82/81 BC. The members of the second Triumvirate – Mark Antony, Octavian and Lepidus – had around three hundred on their hit list in 43/42 BC, most famously the orator Cicero.

12 Milo was convicted of the crime and went into exile. Cicero wrote a speech in his defence (*Pro Milone*) which was never delivered because he was so intimidated by Pompey's soldiers at the courthouse.

13 Catiline. Cicero, who was one of the Consuls in that year, believed that by getting rid of this public enemy, he had acted rightly and saved Rome from disaster. Not everyone agreed with him.

14 Calpurnius Piso. The whole scheme was betrayed and Piso and his accomplices were executed.

15 24 August, AD 79

16 Marcus Vipsanius Agrippa's map of the entire inhabited world as it was known at that time. It was intended as a symbol of the extent of Rome's power under Augustus, since most of the areas shown were under her – and therefore *his* – dominion.

17 Mark Antony. Caesar refused to accept it but that didn't stop him getting killed for his supposed pretensions to tyranny a year later.

18 Masada

19 Flavius Josephus' own experience and eye-witness accounts inform the work, which was completed in AD 79 under the Emperors Vespasian and Titus.

20 1480 years from Augustus in 27 BC to the fall of Constantinople in AD 1453.

BELIEFS AND SUPERSTITIONS

(ANSWERS TO PAGES 45–50)

1 It was the name given to the right-hand horse of a victorious chariot team in the Campus Martius on the 15 October, which was sacrificed to Mars, god of war. The head was displayed on a wall, garlanded with loaves of bread, a custom which was believed to ensure the fertility of the crops.

2 They were a college of priests with distinctive cone-shaped hats and figure-of-eight shaped shields, who performed ritual songs and dances in March and October in honour of the god Mars. The word *salio* in Latin means 'I jump' and the title *Salii* refers to their type of dance, which probably involved a lot of springing and leaping about. A particular favourite was the *tripudium*, a dance in triple time for which the Arval Brethren and some sacred chickens joined in.

3 The Fordicidia was on 16 April. The word *forda* refers to the 'pregnant cow'. Its unborn calf was taken and burned by the Senior Vestal Virgin. The ashes were then mixed with the dried blood of the October Horse to sprinkle on the bonfires of the Parilia, for purification of the sheep.

4 The term was *fas*. The opposite was *nefas*, from which we get the word 'nefarious'. The concept of *fas* and *nefas* dominated the Roman calendar and restricted certain types of activities on certain days.

5 The title *Pontifex Maximus* was ultimately taken over by the Pope (Chief Pontiff) at the end of the fourth century AD.

6 It was called the Lupercalia. Plutarch tells us that pregnant women deliberately presented their hands to the Wolf-men for striking, convinced that it would help them have an easy birth.

7 The *pomerium* was the sacred boundary of a city. The dead were buried outside the city gates as they were considered unholy.

BELIEFS AND
SUPERSTITIONS
(ANSWERS TO PAGES 45–50)

8 The *genius* was the 'spirit' of a place or the father of the
household (*paterfamilias*). It was represented in art by a snake,
sometimes bearded to indicate its maleness.

9 The Isiacus was the priest of the Egyptian goddess Isis.
Wanted criminals were known to have tried to evade justice
by disguising themselves in this way.

10 The cult was called Mithraism. Mithras the Bull-Slayer was
mentioned in Persian folklore and was worshipped in secret
underground caverns, mainly by soldiers in the Roman army.

11 The *lamia* was a female monster or 'bogey-woman' invented
by the Romans to keep their children in line. She was
believed to prowl around devouring children and always had
one in her stomach.

12 (d) To the ancient Druids of Britain mistletoe was a sacred
symbol with both magical powers and medicinal properties.
The custom of hanging up mistletoe probably stems from the
Druid tradition of laying down arms and exchanging
greetings under the mistletoe. The Romans threw all sorts of
things into wishing wells, including coins and inscribed
tablets, with the hope of bringing good luck to themselves or
bad luck to others. Holly was believed to protect against
poison, storms, fire and the 'evil eye'. The Romans had a
thing about thresholds in general: they never crossed one
with the left foot and took great care not to trip. If they did,
they probably used to touch wood.

13 Augury was the art of reading signs and portents, usually
from the flight of birds. Numa Pompilius was the king who
was believed to have set up a number of religious institutions,
including augury.

14 (a) *Flamen Martialis*
(b) *Flamen Dialis*. The title Flamen is probably connected
with the Indo-European 'Brahmin'.

BELIEFS AND
SUPERSTITIONS

15 The *penates* were gods of the store-cupboard worshipped on special days and at every meal. Each household by definition had their own but there were also *penates* of the state (*publici di*) and the Imperial family, which everyone worshipped at the temple of Vesta. They were worshipped in conjunction with the *lares*, the household ghosts.

16 It was literally 'the boat of Isis' but was in fact a brightly-coloured replica of a ship, which was launched on 5 March as the climax of a hugely popular festival to mark the start of the sailing season. The ship didn't actually go anywhere; it was merely allowed to drift out of sight.

17 (a) True. The latter half of June was considered to be the most propitious time.
   (b) False. *Deductio* did in fact have its origins in the legendary Rape of the Sabine Women and did involve the 'snatching' of a bride but, in this case, the man was already married to her and simply pretended to wrest her from her mother's arms as part of the marriage ritual. It helped if the ladies weren't quite expecting it and contributed greatly to the hilarity of the proceedings.
   (c) True. Funerals and weddings were seen as excellent opportunities for such buffoonery and irreverence. It is unlikely that the speech given by a best man at a wedding today would be quite as coarse as the Romans were used to but this modern custom may have had its origins in Roman practice.
   (d) False. *Sex crines* actually refers to the distinctive hair-style of a Roman bride, which was divided at spear-point (*hasta caelibaris*) into six plaits.
   (e) True. This was called the *conclamatio*.

(f) False. Hallowe'en is the eve of All Saints Day, a Christian festival which postdates the Roman era. However, the Romans did have a similar festival in May called the Lemuria and recognised at least two other occasions in the year when they believed that ghosts walked abroad.

18 (d)

19 (a) It is in fact a Tuscan-Latin incantation, probably related to *ardeo* meaning 'I burn' and *averto* meaning 'I ward off'.

20 (b)

ROMAN EMPERORS

(ANSWERS TO PAGES 51–54)

1 Augustus (Emperor 27 BC–AD 14) The birth of Jesus is now believed to have taken place c4 BC.

2 Tiberius (Emperor AD 14–37)

3 Hadrian. The wall of Hadrian, designed to separate Romans and barbarians, was the most elaborate imperial boundary line. Substantial remains can still be seen between modern Newcastle and Carlisle.

4 Suetonius

5 AD 69. Galba, Otho, Vitellius and Vespasian, who ruled for a further ten years

6 *Sextilis* or the 'sixth' month of the year, as it was then. July was called *Quintilis* until it was re-named after Julius Caesar.

7 Domitian (Emperor AD 81–96) The writers Juvenal and Tacitus, in particular, demonstrated an ill-disguised loathing for him in their work. However, they were prudent enough to wait until the Emperor was dead before publishing it!

8 (a) Great-uncle and great-nephew
  (b) Great-uncle and great-nephew
  (c) Brothers
  (d) Father and son

9 Nero (Emperor AD 54–68)

10 Gaius Caligula (Emperor AD 37–41). As a small child, Gaius had been given this endearing nickname meaning 'Bootee', which hardly suited his sadistic and capricious adult behaviour. His cruel regime was cut short by a death blow from his own Praetorian Guard.

11 Tiberius

12 Claudius

13 Julius Caesar, Augustus, Claudius, Vespasian and Titus all became *Divus* after their death. Whether an Emperor achieved this status depended very much on his successor.

Vespasian's words on his deathbed were 'Oh dear! I think I'm becoming a god!'

14 (a) Nero. Poppaea was his mistress long before they married. There are strong suggestions that Nero had his mother and first wife killed at her insistence. Eventually she and her unborn child proved to be two more of his victims when Nero furiously kicked her to death.

(b) Claudius. Messalina is famous for the enormity of her sexual appetite and indiscretions, which included marrying a man whilst she was still married to the Emperor. Claudius was ignorant and ultimately incredulous of her behaviour and so it was one of his advisers who demanded her execution, which she pre-empted by killing herself.

(c) Augustus. Livia was allowed to play an unusually prominent role in the Augustan regime but not everyone viewed her influence on the Emperor as being beneficial. Many believed that she ruthlessly engineered Augustus' affairs, even to the extent of poisoning his potential heirs, in order to further the interests of her own son – and future Emperor – Tiberius.

15 Commodus (Emperor AD 180–92)

16 Tiberius. The historians Tacitus and, in particular, Suetonius catalogue with relish and disgust the Emperor's supposed sexual proclivities and outrageous behaviour, which are largely unfounded.

17 Trajan (Emperor AD 98–117). The Romans called this part of the world Dacia.

18 Constantine (Emperor AD 306–37)

19 Marcus Aurelius (Emperor AD 161–80) wrote his *Meditations* offering much sensible advice and reflection on life.

20 Romulus Augustulus (Emperor AD 475–6)

FOOD AND DINING

1 (a) True
  (b) False
  (c) True, but it was considered bad manners.
  (d) True
  (e) True. It was so common that there were 'sweeper' slaves
      (*scoparii*) with shaven heads who collected and cleared it
      away.
  (f) False. They enjoyed various grades of bread but tomatoes
      were completely unknown to the Romans.
  (g) False. They actually began at the 9th hour – about the
      middle of the afternoon – and often went on all night.
  (h) True
  (i) True. This was another custom they acquired from the
      Greeks.
  (j) False. Citrus fruit cultivation was not introduced to Italy
      from the east until the end of the 2nd century AD.

2 Wine. This was the ancient predecessor of the wine bar. It
  may also have been possible to get snacks here.

3 Dormice (*glires*) were kept in farms and force-fed on
  walnuts, acorns and chestnuts to improve their flavour. The
  Romans also had specially controlled environments in which
  they reared fish (*piscinae*), game (*aviaria*), and hares
  (*leporaria*).

4 Fish and fish entrails which had been allowed to ferment,
  liquefy and drain away from the dregs (*allec*) to make a pungent
  liquid, used as a sauce to flavour dishes or drunk on its own.

5 (a) Salt
  (b) Vinegar (the picture at the top of p. 57 shows the lid of
  one of these)

6 (a) Breakfast
  (b) Lunch

7 He was a young and faithful slave – 'a boy at one's feet' –
  brought from home to attend to all his master's needs at a
  banquet.

8 (j) Turkey, though chicken was not widely eaten either and only a certain variety of parrot (the *psittacus*) was considered edible. Flamingo and lark were particularly enjoyed for their tongues and peacock was considered the height of gastronomic glory.

9 (c) Alexander the Great told of seeing the sages of India eating a fruit which closely resembled the banana. However, the fruit never caught on with the ancient Romans.

10 Dessert. The phrase literally means 'second table'.

LITERATURE

1 Martial – a typical example would be, *Nec tecum possum vivere nec sine te* 'I can't live with you and I can't live without you'.

2 Apuleius. The basic story is that of a young man Lucius who, through his desire to discover the secrets of witchcraft, is transformed into an ass and undergoes colourful adventures. The novel is also known as *Metamorphoses*.

3 Apicius. The recipe collection actually dates from the fourth century AD (Apicius was alive under Augustus and Tiberius) but it clearly meant something to have Apicius' name connected with it.

4 Livy

5 Horace. The poem was the literary epistle *Ars Poetica*.

6 Petronius Arbiter. Tacitus' account of his character would seem to suggest that he was the author of this work but the evidence is not conclusive.

7 (a) Vitruvius
   (b) Frontinus

8 Terence. Like Plautus before him, Terence based his work on the models in Greek New Comedy, written by the likes of Menander.

9 (a) Catullus
   (b) Ovid
   (c) Propertius
   (d) Tibullus

10 Catullus

11 *De Rerum Natura* or *On the Nature of Things*. Tackling such heady subjects as physics and metaphysics, this poem is the quintessential expression of the Epicurean belief that the universe can be understood.

12 Julius Caesar, *De bello Gallico* starts 'The whole of Gaul is divided into three parts …'

13 To have his poem the *Aeneid* destroyed! Virgil had spent the last ten years of his life composing it and was intending to spend a further three correcting it. Thankfully, he did not get his dying wish granted and the poem, even in its own day, became a Roman classic.

14 Ennius. He liked to style himself as the reincarnation of Homer and was certainly outstanding amongst Latin poets at least for the quantity and breadth of his creative output.

15 Seneca

16 Ovid. The elegies were known as *Amores*. Ovid's saucy didactic work *Ars Amatoria* got him into hot water with the Emperor Augustus. Ovid strongly denied luring chaste people into erotic intrigues but his constant appeals fell on deaf ears. He was sent into exile and never allowed to return to Rome.

17 *Aulularia* or *The Pot of Gold*

18 Tacitus

19 The orator Cicero. His *Consulship* contains the famously awful line, *o fortunatam natam me consule Romam*, which translates as 'O happy Rome, to have been born in my Consulship!'

20 *Naturalis Historia* or *Natural History*. Pliny the Younger gives us a fascinating insight into his uncle's energetic and diligent working habits.

— LATIN IN USE TODAY —

(ANSWERS TO PAGES 63–66)

1 (a) *id est* – that is (by way of explanation)
   (b) *exempli gratia* – for example (by way of example)
   (c) *per annum* – per year
   (d) *quod erat demonstrandum* – which was to be demonstrated
   (e) *post scriptum* – after it (the letter) has been written
   (f) *per procurationem* – by the agency of
   (g) *nota bene* – note well
   (h) *requiescat in pace* – may he (or she) rest in peace
   (i) *anno domini* – in the year of our Lord
   (j) *curriculum vitae* – course of life

2 (a) 140
   (b) 1500
   (c) 66
   (d) 1900

3 (a) For this special purpose
   (b) To infinity

4 (a) *(in) flagrante delicto*
   (b) *habeas corpus*

5 On an unspecified day

6 (a) *videlicet* – namely
   (b) *scilicet* – namely
   (c) *et cetera* – and the rest
   (d) *ad libitum* – at pleasure, freely
   (e) *et alia* – and the rest
   (f) *pro / contra* – for / against
   (g) *vox populi* – voice (opinion) of the people
   (h) *ibidem* – in the same place
   (i) *confer* – compare
   (j) *loco citato* – at the place quoted

7 *lingua franca*

8 *annus horribilis*

9 To warn the 'buyer to beware' of the deal he is entering into
   – eg when buying antiques.

10 (a) Royal Marines – By sea, by land
   (b) Royal Air Force – Through adversity to the stars
   (c) The Olympics – Swifter, higher, stronger
   (d) Metro Goldwyn Mayer – Art for art's sake

11 (a) A temporary 'replacement'
   (b) A guardian, 'in place of a parent'

12 *tabula rasa*

13 *verbatim*

14 *Deo volente*

15 *compos mentis*

16 It is taken orally, 'with the living voice'.

17 'Everywhere', throughout the book, or work

18 Nothing, *gratis* means 'free'.

19 It is trustworthy and can be taken 'in good faith'.

20 By putting it 'the other way round'.

ART AND
ARCHITECTURE
(ANSWERS TO PAGES 67–70)

1 (c) The colossal statue was in the vestibule which linked the Forum with Nero's extravagant residence The Golden Palace which was erected after the Great Fire of Rome.

2 (c) *peculium* is a legal term for 'assets', *tablinum* is the master's room or 'study', *atrium* is the central open area or 'hallway' of the house and *peristylium* is a garden surrounded by a colonnade.

3 Beautiful examples of mosaic pavements. The House of the Faun housed the magnificent Alexander Mosaic now in Naples Archaeological Museum. At Palestrina an exotic scene from the Nile is one of the main subjects. Among the many scenes depicted at Piazza Amerina are animal hunts and chariot racing.

4 Chichester, known to the Romans as Noviomagus. The villa, with its fine Roman mosaics, may have been built for the British client-king Cogidubnus, in gratitude for his long-standing loyalty to the Emperor.

5 Pompey

6 Acanthus

7 Basilica. Both buildings were designed in a rectangular plan divided by two rows of columns into a central nave and two aisles.

8 The Circus Maximus. The *carceres* are the 'starting gates' and the *metae* the 'turning-posts' at either end of the *spina*, the long central barrier which was frequently decorated with obelisks, monuments and the movable eggs and dolphins which marked the seven laps.

9 The Baths of Caracalla

10 (c) The Circus Maximus could hold 250,000 spectators.

11 Trajan's Column. A replica can be seen in the Victoria and Albert Museum in London.

12 The Pantheon

13 False. There is evidence, for example from Herculaneum and Pompeii, that from the first century AD the Romans had glazed windows.

14 They imitated the shape of primitive houses or huts.

15 The *Ara Pacis (Augustae)*. The altar commemorated Augustus' safe return from Spain and Gaul in 13 BC. The monument was reconstructed during the 1930s on the banks of the river Tiber near the Mausoleum of Augustus.

16 The Maison Carrée. Nemausus (Nîmes) was the seat of an important Roman mint and boasts some significant remains, which include an amphitheatre and this Corinthian temple dedicated to Augustus' grandsons, Gaius and Lucius.

17 They are all modern interpretations of the Roman triumphal arch. The London and Paris examples are respectively Marble Arch and The Arc de Triomphe. The Washington Square Arch was first erected as a temporary wood-and-plaster structure but the Arch was so popular that money was raised to put up a permanent version.

18 Marcus Aurelius

19 Pompeian Red

20 The Portland Vase. The Romans produced many exquisite examples of cameo work, often, like the Portland Vase, with complex and obscure mythological scenes. Such vases inspired the famous and ever-popular blue and white jasperware of Josiah Wedgwood, whose crowning achievement was his reproduction of the Portland Vase in 1790 after four years of laborious trials.

WHAT DOES IT
REALLY MEAN?
(ANSWERS TO PAGES 71–74)

1 (c) that's how the world's glory passes

2 (a) Ariadne gave him a sword

3 (b) Caesar, having chanced upon a favourable wind

4 (b) Hail, O Lord

5 (a) in the place of a parent

6 (b) nothing beyond it

7 (c) 80

8 (b) in the year of our Lord

9 (a) there's no accounting for tastes

10 (b) beneath one's dignity

11 (c) at first sight

12 (b) thee O God

13 (c) where there's life, there's hope

14 (a) (say) nothing but good about the dead

15 (c) let the buyer beware

16 (a) more haste, less speed

17 (b) dogs are the guardians of houses

18 (a) note well

19 (b) to sound the retreat

20 (c) boys, learn to have compassion for the poor

1 *Spartacus*

2 (a) Nero in *Quo Vadis*
  (b) Lentulus Batiatus in *Spartacus*

3 Sophia Loren

4 (a) *Ben-Hur*
  (b) The Director was William Wyler. Charlton Heston and
      Hugh Griffith won Best Actor and Supporting Actor
      respectively.

5 (a) Richard Burton
  (b) *Demetrius and the Gladiators* (1954)
  (c) Demetrius

6 (a) Malcolm McDowell
  (b) Emperor Tiberius

7 (a) Warren William
  (b) Rex Harrison
  (c) Claude Rains
  (d) Marlon Brando
  (e) Kenneth Williams, delivering the immortal line 'Infamy!
      Infamy! They've all got it in-for-me!'

8 Cecil B. De Mille

9 Charles Laughton

10 *Fellini Satyricon*

11 Stephen Boyd

12 (a) Claudette Colbert
   (b) Elizabeth Taylor
   (c) Vivien Leigh
   (d) Amanda Barrie

13 (a) *A Funny Thing Happened on the Way to the Forum*

(b)   Richard Lester, fresh from directing two of The Beatles'
      movies
(c)   Zero Mostel

14 (a)   Basil Rathbone
    (b)   Telly Savalas
    (c)   Donald Pleasence

15 (a)   Marcus Aurelius
    (b)   Commodus

16 (a)   Henry Wilcoxon
    (b)   Richard Burton
    (c)   Charlton Heston
    (d)   Sid James

17 '*Romani, ite domum!*' or 'Romans, go home!' Brian at first
    writes, '*Romani eunt domus*' until his syntax is corrected by a
    passing Roman soldier, played as an old-style Latin master by
    the inimitable John Cleese.

18 *Ben-Hur* (1925) cost a staggering $3.9 million.

19 *Quo Vadis*. *Cleopatra* (1963) came close with a remarkable
    26,000 costumes.

20 *The Fall of the Roman Empire* (1964)

ROMANS AT WAR

1 (a) King Pyrrhus of Epirus.
  (b) He defeated the Romans at three successive battles but incurred heavy casualties in the process, returning to Epirus with less than one third of his original force.

2 The Punic Wars, so-called because the Romans called the Carthaginian enemy *Poeni*.

3 Hannibal

4 An eye

5 Cannae. The Romans were outflanked and virtually surrounded by the enemy, possibly suffering more casualties in just one day's fighting than any other western army ever since.

6 (a) *Cunctator* or 'Delayer'
  (b) Fabian tactics

7 Publius Cornelius Scipio received the cognomen *Africanus*.

8 Marius

9 Sulla. He was not interested in remaining in power but just wanted to reform what he saw as a corrupt Senate.

10 Her *socii* or Italian 'allies'. Rome won only by granting citizenship to everyone in Italy south of the River Po.

11 Pompey

12 Carrhae. Crassus' death helped to bring Julius Caesar and Pompey, the two remaining Triumvirs, into the conflict that led to civil war.

13 The Gallic War was the name that Julius Caesar, the victorious commander of the Roman forces, gave to his own account of the conflict.

14 Julius Caesar and the Gallic leader Vercingetorix.

15 Pharsalus. Pompey fled and was murdered in Egypt.

16 (a) Mark Antony and Octavian
   (b) Cassius and Brutus

17 Actium, which took its name from the cape on the Greek coast, the site of Mark Antony's camp. In less than a year, Egypt was annexed to the Roman Empire.

18 The temple of Janus. The three times were

    (a) during the reign of Numa Pompilius,
    (b) after the second Punic War, and then
    (c) during the early part of the reign of Augustus.

19 Quintilius Varus. The treacherous German war chief Arminius had served a long time in Rome's auxiliary forces and earned Roman citizenship.

20 Gaius Caligula

A GLOSSARY OF NAMES
USED IN THIS BOOK

Augustus Gaius Octavius, later also Julius Caesar Augustus,
Emperor, 63 BC–AD 14

Caesar Gaius Julius Caesar,
General and statesman, 100–44 BC

Catullus Gaius Valerius Catullus,
Poet, c84–54 BC

Cicero Marcus Tullius Cicero,
Orator, 106–43 BC

Ennius Quintus Ennius,
Historian and playwright, 239–169 BC

Horace Quintus Horatius Flaccus,
Poet, 65–8 BC

Livy Titus Livius,
Historian, c64/59 BC– AD 12/17

Lucretius Titus Lucretius Carus,
Poet, c94–c55/51 BC

Mark Antony Marcus Antonius
Statesman, 83–30 BC

Martial Marcus Valerius Martialis,
Poet, cAD 38–c104

Octavian (See Augustus)

Ovid Publius Ovidius Naso,
Poet, 43 BC–AD 17

Plautus Titus Maccius Plautus,
Playwright, 3rd–2nd century BC

Pliny the Elder Gaius Plinius Secundus,
Natural historian, cAD 23/4–79

Pliny the Younger Gaius Plinius Caecilius Secundus,
Writer and statesman, cAD 61–c112

Pompey (the Great) Gnaeus Pompeius Magnus,
Statesman, c106–48 BC

A GLOSSARY OF NAMES
(continued)

Seneca Lucius Annaeus Seneca (the Younger),
  Writer, *c*4 BC/ AD 1–65
Tacitus (? Publius) Cornelius Tacitus,
  Historian, AD 56–*c*120
Terence Publius Terentius Afer,
  Playwright, 3rd–2nd century BC
Virgil Publius Virgilius Maro,
  Poet, 70–19 BC